Pip and Posy

www.worldofpipandposy.com

First published 2014 by Nosy Crow Ltd
The Crow's Nest, 10a Lant Street
London SE1 1QR
www.nosycrow.com

ISBN 978 0 85763 403 0

Nosy Crow and associated logos are trademarks and/or registered
trademarks of Nosy Crow Ltd
Text © Nosy Crow 2014
Illustrations © Axel Scheffler 2012

The right of Axel Scheffler to be identified as the illustrator
of this work has been asserted.

A CIP catalogue record for this book is available from the British Library.

Printed in China

3 5 7 9 8 6 4

Pip and Posy
Look and Say

Axel Scheffler

nosy crow

Pip and Posy love to do
lots of different things!

Can you find these things?

swings

scooter

bench

When they're in the park,
they take it in turns to
ride Pip's scooter.

slide

tree

snail

see-saw

rocker

On sunny days, the friends go shopping
in the town. What a busy place it is!
Today, Pip has bought a big, red balloon.

Can you find these things?

bag

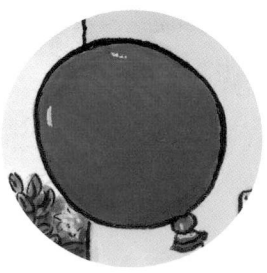

balloon

oranges

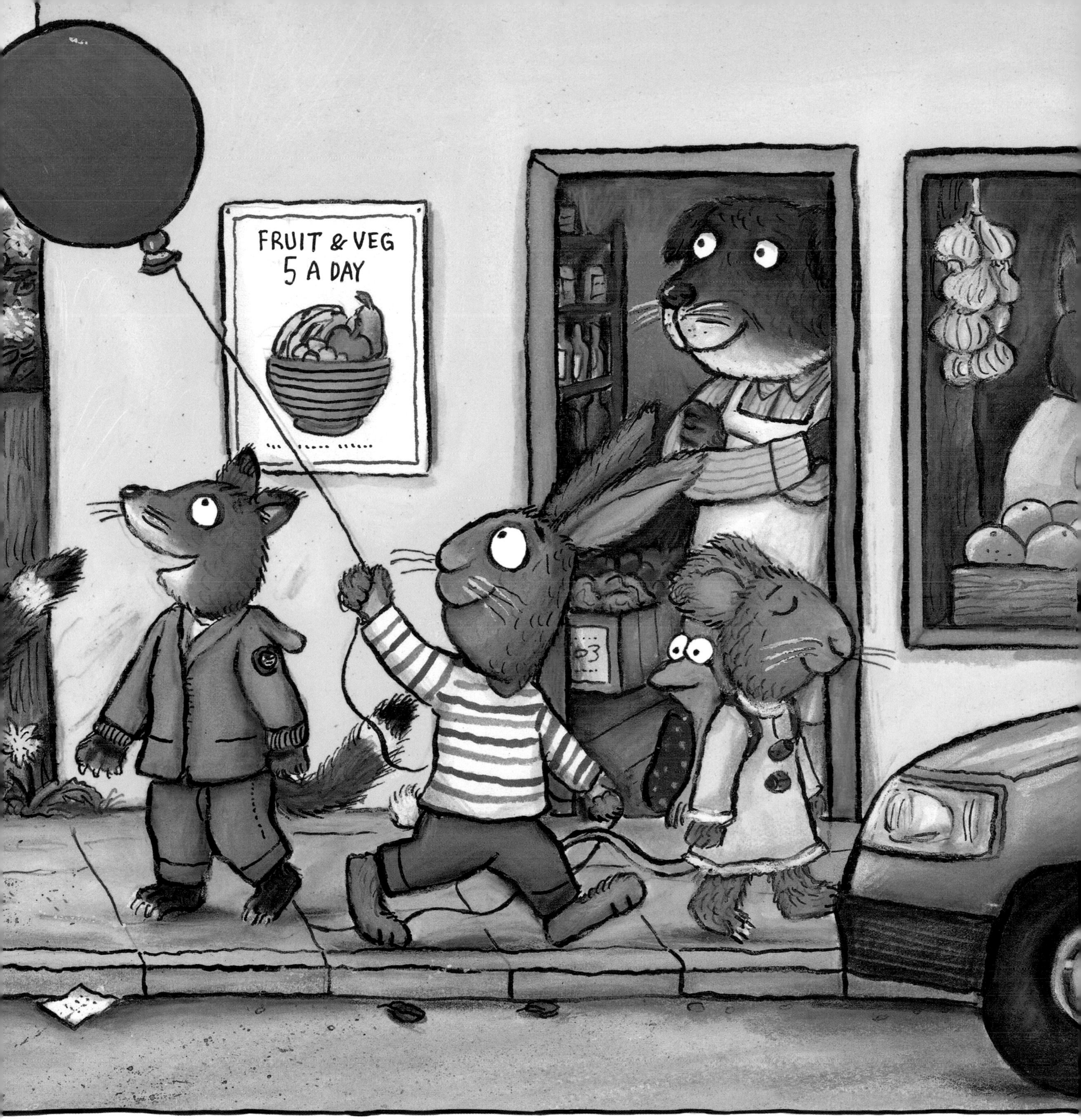
FRUIT & VEG
5 A DAY

pigeon

helmet

fish

FRUIT & VEG
5 A DAY
poster

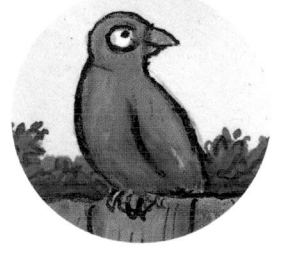

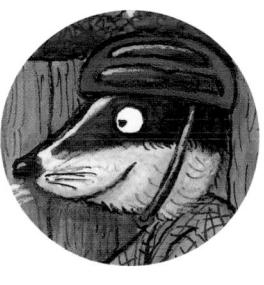

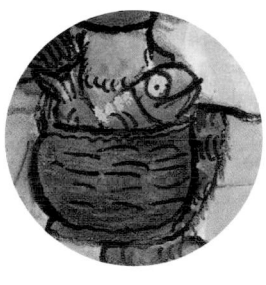

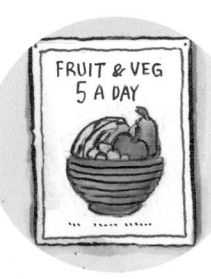

bicycle

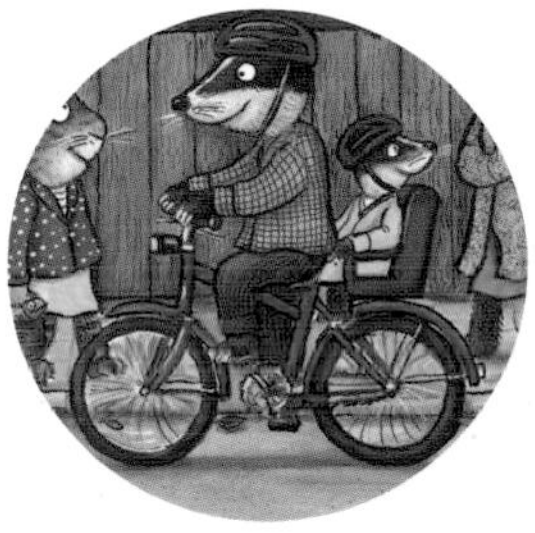

But playing in the sandpit is much more fun than shopping.

 Can you find these things?

 rucksack

 flower

 frog

Sometimes they build
a really big sandcastle!

bee

house

spade

pushchair

bucket

Can you find these things?

bird

leaf

slug

On rainy days, Pip and Posy prefer to stay indoors. Nobody likes playing in the wet.

watering can

fence

pear

Posy

broom

But when it snows, everyone loves to play outside!

 **Can you find these things?**

 sledge

 hat

 coat

Look how fast Pip and Posy's sledge goes!

"Wheeeeee!"

they shout.

robin

glasses

boots

mittens

scarf

Back inside, they take off their
coats and boots. It's so nice
to be in the warm again!

 Can you find these things?

fruit bowl

picture

telephone

"What would you like to play, Pip?" asks Posy.

door handle

keys

wellies

vase

letter

Pip and Posy always get out
ALL their toys when they play!
Pip especially loves the train track.
"Woo! Woo!" he says.

Can you find these things?

sheep

car

horse

Posy likes to build towers. She puts
the bricks on very carefully.

train

cat

building block

bear

dinosaur

After all that fun, it's time for everyone to have a snack, even the toys!

Can you find these things?

fork

cake

apple

Pip has a lovely, cool drink and some crunchy carrot sticks.

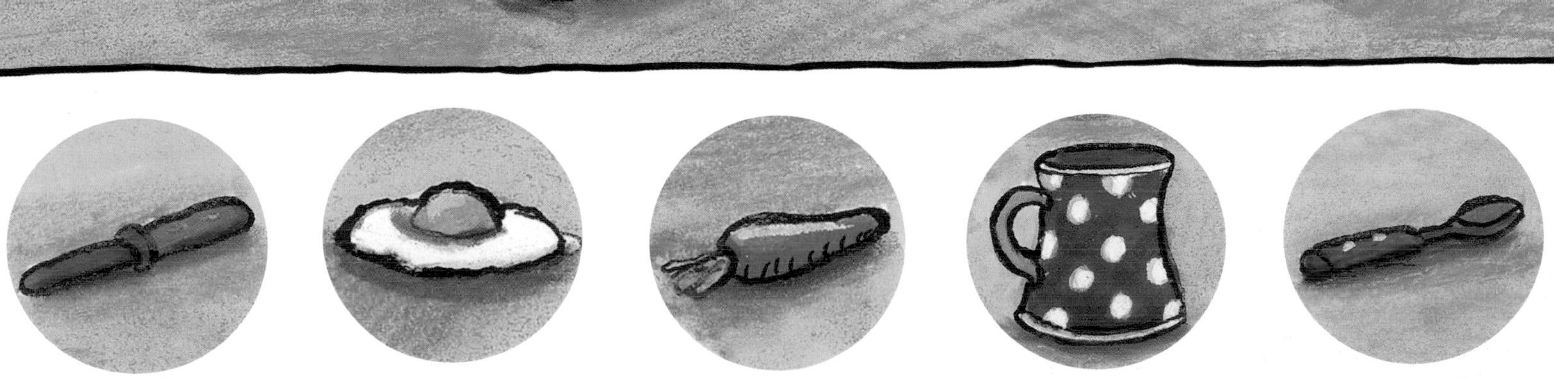

knife 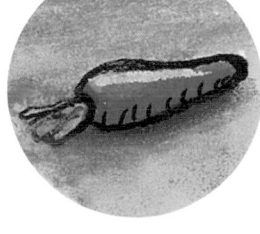 egg  carrot  mug  spoon

Sometimes, Pip dresses up as a furry monster.
"I'm coming to tickle you, Posy!" he calls.

Can you find these things?

cushion

jug

curtains

Posy thinks this is
very funny indeed!

bookcase

light switch

doormat

coat hooks

armchair

Pip and Posy's most favourite thing of all
is playing with their play-dough.

Can you find these things?

fireplace

crocodile

painting

Look at all the different animals they've made!

pig

penguin

elephant

cupboard

giraffe

No matter where they are,
or what they do . . .

 Can you find these things?

path

chimney

daisy

. . . Pip and Posy always
look after each other.

beetle

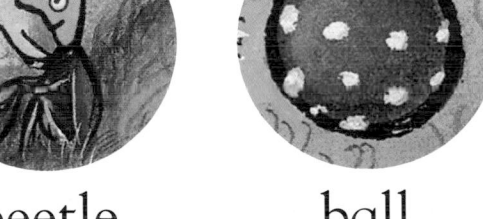
ball

worm

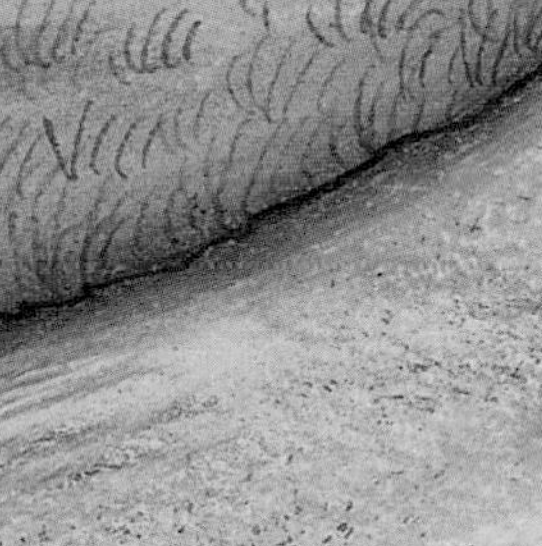

nest

window

And how do Pip and Posy
like to finish a day of fun?
With a lovely, warm bath . . .

 Can you find these things?

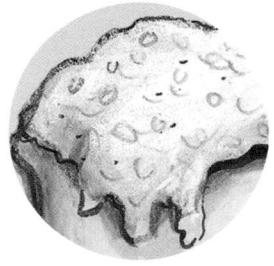 bubbles

 sock

 shampoo

. . . and lots, and lots of bubbles!

Hooray!

duck

toilet

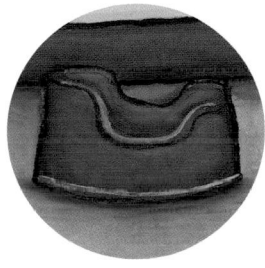
potty

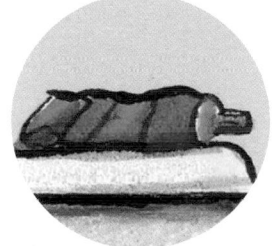
toothpaste

toilet roll